TURNING OFF MY
HUNGER
Switch

A Daily Journal

PAUL RIVAS, M.D.

D1441281

PRENTICE HALL
Paramus, New Jersey 07652

Day of the week: _____ Date: _____

Medication/
Supplement   **Dosage**   **Time**

_____

_____

_____

Side Effects:

_____

_____

Foods Consumed:

_____

_____

Appetite Changes and Moods:

_____

_____

_____

Journal Comments:

_____

_____

_____

_____

_____

_____

_____

Day of the week: _____ Date: _____

Medication/
Supplement   Dosage   Time

_____

_____

_____

Side Effects:

_____

_____

Foods Consumed:

_____

_____

Appetite Changes and Moods:

_____

_____

_____

Journal Comments:

_____

_____

_____

_____

_____

_____

_____

Day of the week: _____ Date: _____

**Medication/
Supplement**   Dosage   Time

_____

_____

_____

Side Effects:

_____

_____

Foods Consumed:

_____

_____

Appetite Changes and Moods:

_____

_____

_____

Journal Comments:

_____

_____

_____

_____

_____

_____

_____

**Medication/
Supplement**   Dosage   Time

_____

_____

_____

Side Effects:

_____

_____

Foods Consumed:

_____

_____

Appetite Changes and Moods:

_____

_____

_____

Journal Comments:

_____

_____

_____

_____

_____

_____

_____

Day of the week: _____ Date: _____

**Medication/
Supplement**   **Dosage**   **Time**

_____

_____

_____

Side Effects:

_____

_____

Foods Consumed:

_____

_____

Appetite Changes and Moods:

_____

_____

_____

Journal Comments:

_____

_____

_____

_____

_____

_____

_____

Day of the week: _____   Date: _____

Medication/
Supplement   **Dosage**   **Time**

_____

_____

_____

Side Effects:

_____

_____

Foods Consumed:

_____

_____

Appetite Changes and Moods:

_____

_____

_____

Journal Comments:

_____

_____

_____

_____

_____

_____

Day of the week: _____ Date: _____

**Medication/
Supplement**   Dosage   Time

_____

_____

_____

Side Effects:

_____

_____

Foods Consumed:

_____

_____

Appetite Changes and Moods:

_____

_____

_____

Journal Comments:

_____

_____

_____

_____

_____

_____

_____

Day of the week: _____ Date: _____

Medication/
Supplement   Dosage   Time

_____

_____

_____

Side Effects:

_____

_____

Foods Consumed:

_____

_____

Appetite Changes and Moods:

_____

_____

_____

Journal Comments:

_____

_____

_____

_____

_____

_____

_____

Day of the week: _____ Date: _____

Medication/
Supplement   Dosage   Time

_____

_____

_____

Side Effects:

_____

_____

Foods Consumed:

_____

_____

Appetite Changes and Moods:

_____

_____

_____

Journal Comments:

_____

_____

_____

_____

_____

_____

_____

Day of the week: _____ Date: _____

Medication/
Supplement   Dosage   Time

_____

_____

_____

Side Effects:

_____

_____

Foods Consumed:

_____

_____

Appetite Changes and Moods:

_____

_____

_____

Journal Comments:

_____

_____

_____

_____

_____

_____

_____

Day of the week: _____   Date: _____

Medication/
Supplement   **Dosage**   **Time**

_____

_____

_____

Side Effects:

_____

_____

Foods Consumed:

_____

_____

Appetite Changes and Moods:

_____

_____

_____

Journal Comments:

_____

_____

_____

_____

_____

_____

_____

Day of the week: _____ Date: _____

Medication/
Supplement   Dosage   Time

_____

_____

_____

Side Effects:

_____

_____

Foods Consumed:

_____

_____

Appetite Changes and Moods:

_____

_____

_____

Journal Comments:

_____

_____

_____

_____

_____

_____

_____

_____

Day of the week: _____ Date: _____

**Medication/
Supplement**   **Dosage**   **Time**

_____

_____

_____

Side Effects:

_____

_____

Foods Consumed:

_____

_____

Appetite Changes and Moods:

_____

_____

_____

Journal Comments:

_____

_____

_____

_____

_____

_____

_____

Day of the week: _____ Date: _____

Medication/
Supplement   Dosage   Time

_____
_____
_____

Side Effects:

_____
_____

Foods Consumed:

_____
_____

Appetite Changes and Moods:

_____
_____
_____

Journal Comments:

_____
_____
_____
_____
_____
_____
_____

Day of the week: _____ Date: _____

**Medication/
Supplement**   Dosage   Time

_____

_____

_____

Side Effects:

_____

_____

Foods Consumed:

_____

_____

Appetite Changes and Moods:

_____

_____

_____

Journal Comments:

_____

_____

_____

_____

_____

_____

_____

_____

Day of the week: _____   Date: _____

Medication/
Supplement   Dosage   Time

_____

_____

_____

Side Effects:

_____

_____

Foods Consumed:

_____

_____

Appetite Changes and Moods:

_____

_____

_____

Journal Comments:

_____

_____

_____

_____

_____

_____

_____

_____

Day of the week: _____ Date: _____

**Medication/
Supplement**   Dosage   Time

_____

_____

_____

Side Effects:

_____

_____

Foods Consumed:

_____

_____

Appetite Changes and Moods:

_____

_____

_____

Journal Comments:

_____

_____

_____

_____

_____

_____

_____

Day of the week: _____   Date: _____

Medication/
Supplement   **Dosage**   **Time**

_____

_____

_____

Side Effects:

_____

_____

Foods Consumed:

_____

_____

Appetite Changes and Moods:

_____

_____

_____

Journal Comments:

_____

_____

_____

_____

_____

_____

_____

Day of the week: _____ Date: _____

Medication/
Supplement   Dosage   Time

_____

_____

_____

Side Effects:

_____

_____

Foods Consumed:

_____

_____

Appetite Changes and Moods:

_____

_____

_____

Journal Comments:

_____

_____

_____

_____

_____

_____

_____

Day of the week: _____   Date: _____

**Medication/
Supplement**   **Dosage**   **Time**

_____

_____

_____

Side Effects:

_____

_____

Foods Consumed:

_____

_____

Appetite Changes and Moods:

_____

_____

_____

Journal Comments:

_____

_____

_____

_____

_____

_____

_____

Day of the week: _____ Date: _____

**Medication/
Supplement**   Dosage   Time

_____

_____

_____

Side Effects:

_____

_____

Foods Consumed:

_____

_____

Appetite Changes and Moods:

_____

_____

_____

Journal Comments:

_____

_____

_____

_____

_____

_____

_____

Day of the week: _____ Date: _____

Medication/
Supplement   **Dosage**   **Time**

_____

_____

_____

Side Effects:

_____

_____

Foods Consumed:

_____

_____

Appetite Changes and Moods:

_____

_____

_____

Journal Comments:

_____

_____

_____

_____

_____

_____

_____

Day of the week: _____ Date: _____

**Medication/
Supplement**   Dosage   Time

_____

_____

_____

Side Effects:

_____

_____

Foods Consumed:

_____

_____

Appetite Changes and Moods:

_____

_____

_____

Journal Comments:

_____

_____

_____

_____

_____

_____

_____

Day of the week: _____ Date: _____

**Medication/
Supplement**   **Dosage**   **Time**

_____

_____

_____

Side Effects:

_____

_____

Foods Consumed:

_____

_____

Appetite Changes and Moods:

_____

_____

_____

Journal Comments:

_____

_____

_____

_____

_____

_____

_____

Day of the week: _____ Date: _____

Medication/
Supplement   Dosage   Time

_____

_____

_____

Side Effects:

_____

_____

Foods Consumed:

_____

_____

Appetite Changes and Moods:

_____

_____

_____

Journal Comments:

_____

_____

_____

_____

_____

_____

_____

**Medication/
Supplement**   **Dosage**   **Time**

_____

_____

_____

Side Effects:

_____

_____

Foods Consumed:

_____

_____

Appetite Changes and Moods:

_____

_____

_____

Journal Comments:

_____

_____

_____

_____

_____

_____

_____

Day of the week: _____   Date: _____

Medication/
Supplement   **Dosage**   **Time**

_____

_____

_____

Side Effects:

_____

_____

Foods Consumed:

_____

_____

Appetite Changes and Moods:

_____

_____

_____

Journal Comments:

_____

_____

_____

_____

_____

_____

_____

Day of the week: _____ Date: _____

Medication/
Supplement   **Dosage**   **Time**

_____

_____

_____

Side Effects:

_____

_____

Foods Consumed:

_____

_____

Appetite Changes and Moods:

_____

_____

_____

Journal Comments:

_____

_____

_____

_____

_____

_____

_____

Day of the week: _____   Date: _____

Medication/
Supplement   **Dosage**   **Time**

_____

_____

_____

Side Effects:

_____

_____

Foods Consumed:

_____

_____

Appetite Changes and Moods:

_____

_____

_____

Journal Comments:

_____

_____

_____

_____

_____

_____

_____

Day of the week: _____   Date: _____

Medication/
Supplement   **Dosage**   **Time**

_____

_____

_____

Side Effects:

_____

_____

Foods Consumed:

_____

_____

Appetite Changes and Moods:

_____

_____

_____

Journal Comments:

_____

_____

_____

_____

_____

_____

Day of the week: _____ Date: _____

Medication/
Supplement   Dosage   Time

_____

_____

_____

Side Effects:

_____

_____

Foods Consumed:

_____

_____

Appetite Changes and Moods:

_____

_____

_____

Journal Comments:

_____

_____

_____

_____

_____

_____

_____

ISBN 0-13-044661-0